Please return this book on or before the date shown above. To
renew go to www.essex.gov.uk/libraries, ring 0845 603 7628 or
go to any Essex library.

Essex County Council

MACMILLAN

30130 140472142

MACMILLAN READERS

BEGINNER LEVEL

Founding Editor: John Milne

The Macmillan Readers provide a choice of enjoyable reading materials for learners of English. The series is published at six levels – Starter, Beginner, Elementary, Pre-intermediate, Intermediate and Upper.

Level control

Information, structure and vocabulary are controlled to suit the students' ability at each level.

The number of words at each level:

Starter	about 300 basic words
Beginner	about 600 basic words
Elementary	about 1100 basic words
Pre-intermediate	about 1400 basic words
Intermediate	about 1600 basic words
Upper	about 2200 basic words

Vocabulary

Some difficult words and phrases in this book are important for understanding the story. Some of these words are explained in the story and some are shown in the pictures. From Pre-intermediate level upwards, words are marked with a number like this: ...³. These words are explained in the Glossary at the end of the book.

Part 1

It was a beautiful summer evening. Paul was happy. No more exams. College was finished. Now he needed a job. He wanted to be a writer and work for a newspaper. But first he needed a rest.

It was hot in the house. There was no wind.

I'll go for a walk, said Paul to himself. I'll go down to the river.

Paul lived in a small town and he was soon outside in the country. He walked near the river and watched the water birds.

Suddenly he saw the girl. She was standing alone, looking into the water. She was young, and very beautiful. She had long dark hair, and she was wearing a pretty white dress.

Paul went up to her.

'Hello,' he said. 'What's your name?'

'I'm Maria,' she said, and she smiled at him.

Paul and Maria talked for a long time. The sun went down. It was nearly dark.

'I must go home,' said Maria.

'Where do you live?' asked Paul.

'In the big white house on the hill,' said Maria. 'Where do you live?'

'In the little brown house near the market,' said Paul.

They laughed. But Paul was sad. The house on the hill was big and important. Maria was rich, and he was poor. And Paul was in love.

After that, Paul and Maria often met near the river. Maria always wore beautiful clothes. She always looked lovely. Paul thought about Maria all day and every day.

One evening, Paul said, 'Listen, Maria, I've written a poem about you.'

He took a piece of paper from his pocket and read the poem.

> I met her in the evening
> By the riverside.
> Her dress was creamy white
> And her hair with ribbon tied.
>
> She turned and smiled at me,
> And I asked her for her name.
> Though I am young and poor,
> My love will stay the same.

'You are wonderful, Paul,' said Maria. 'I love your poem.'

Paul took Maria's hand. He looked into her eyes.

'I love you, Maria,' he said. 'Do you love me?'

She smiled. 'Yes, of course I love you,' she said. She stood up. 'I must go home now.'

Paul was very happy.

She loves me! Maria loves me, he thought.

Paul went home. The little brown house was small and poor. But it was always clean and tidy. Paul lived alone with his mother. His father was dead.

That evening, his mother watched him.

'What's happened, Paul?' she asked. 'Why are you so happy?'

'It's nothing, Mother,' said Paul.

His mother smiled. He's in love, she thought.

The next day, Paul and Maria met again by the river. Maria looked sad, but Paul did not notice. He took her hand.

'Maria,' he said, 'I am poor now, but one day I am going to be a famous writer.' Maria said nothing.

6

'Will you marry me, Maria? Say yes. We will be so happy, and . . .' he stopped.

Maria looked at him for a moment. There were tears in her eyes. Slowly, she shook her head. Then she turned and ran away.

'Maria!' shouted Paul. But Maria had gone.

Paul went home slowly. He did not understand Maria.

What is wrong? he thought. She loves me, doesn't she?

His mother was waiting for him. She saw his face.

Poor boy, she thought. The girl doesn't love him.

Paul and his mother ate their supper in silence. Suddenly somebody knocked on the door. Paul opened it. A man in a servant's uniform stood outside.

'I'm from the house on the hill,' he said. 'My mistress wants to see Paul.'

'That's me,' said Paul.

'Can you come with me now?' said the servant.

'Yes,' said Paul. He was excited.

Perhaps Maria has changed her mind, he thought. Perhaps she does want to marry me.

Paul's mother stood at the door of the house. She watched Paul and the servant.

The house on the hill, she said to herself. I know those people. A rich old woman, and her beautiful daughter. My poor son!

It was not far to the house on the hill. The servant took Paul up the wide steps and into the house. Paul was excited and his heart was beating fast.

Everything was rich and grand. There were beautiful carpets, pictures and mirrors.

Paul saw himself in a mirror. He looked terrible. This place was so rich, and he looked so poor.

The servant opened a door. Paul went inside. An old lady was sitting in a big chair. Maria stood behind her. The old woman was ugly. Her eyes were small and cold, and her mouth was thin and hard. Her old hands were covered with big rings. She looked proud and angry.

Paul looked at the old woman, then at Maria. What an ugly old woman, he thought. Is she Maria's mother?

'So you want to marry my daughter?' the old woman said. Her voice was hard.

Paul looked at her bravely. 'Yes,' he said. 'I love Maria and I want to marry her.'

The old woman laughed.

'You! A poor student! No money, no father, nothing! My daughter will never marry you.'

Paul said nothing. He looked at Maria. She did not look at him.

'I am poor now,' he said. 'But one day I'll be a famous writer.'

The old woman laughed again. 'No,' she said. 'My daughter is not for you. She is going to be married soon. You will never see her again.'

The old woman got up and left the room.

Maria and Paul were alone. Paul looked at Maria, but she did not look at him. She stood still and did not say anything.

Paul went up to her and put his arm round her. Maria moved away from him.

'I'm sorry, Paul,' said Maria. 'My mother is right. I can't marry you. I don't want to be poor. I want money, and clothes, and a big car.'

'But you love me, Maria,' said Paul. 'And I love you.' He did not understand her. He was angry.

'Yes, I love you, Paul,' said Maria. 'But love isn't enough.' She looked at him. Her face was sad.

'I'm getting married in two weeks,' she said. 'Goodbye, Paul. I'm sorry.'

Paul left the big house and ran down the hill to the river. He sat there for a long time.

Maria loves me. I know she loves me, he thought. But she is marrying another man. She is marrying him for money. It's her mother! Maria is afraid of that ugly old woman! Oh Maria, Maria, what shall I do?

After a long time, Paul went home. There was a light in the window of the little house. The door was open. His mother was waiting for him. She looked at his face, then she put her arms round him.

'They are bad people, my son,' she said. 'You must forget her.'

Part 2

For many days, Paul did not see any of his friends. His mother was worried about him. He did not talk to her. He did not eat or sleep. He often went to the river and sat there alone. All the time he thought about Maria.

One day he saw a headline in the newspaper:

RICH MAN'S BEAUTIFUL BRIDE

There was a picture of Maria and her husband. She was wearing a long white dress and a diamond necklace. Her husband was old and fat. Paul turned the newspaper over angrily.

There was a large notice on the back page of the newspaper. It was an advertisement. Paul sat down and read the advertisement carefully.

Story Competition

Write a story and win a prize!

Our story competition offers a chance to young writers to win recognition and earn money. Stories can be on any theme but must not be longer than 1500 words. Send your entry to this newspaper before the end of the month.

FIRST PRIZE £500!
Ten other prizes of £50!

This is my chance! he said to himself. I'll write the story of Paul and Maria. And I'll win the competition. She'll read our story, and she'll be sorry.

Paul was very busy now. Every day he got up early and worked at his story. His mother watched him. She was pleased. He was eating his food again. He was talking and smiling.

Sometimes Paul felt pleased with his story. It was a good story. But sometimes it was difficult to write. He was unhappy and he wanted to stop writing. But he did not stop. At last, the story was finished.

Paul read it to his mother. She was very pleased.

'It's a good story, Paul,' she said. 'It's very good.'

Paul wrote the story out again carefully and sent it to the newspaper.

Two weeks later, a letter came from the newspaper. Paul did not open it. He was too excited. He gave it to his mother.

'You read it for me, Mother,' he said.

His mother opened the letter and read it.

'Read it yourself,' she said, and gave it to him. She was laughing and crying too.

Paul read the letter.

THE CLARION NEWS
34 Royal Avenue Morse East Lavi
Phone 1214051 & 1293384

Dear Sir,

I am very happy to inform you that you have won first prize in the story competition.

If you would kindly call at this office on Thursday at 10 am, the Manager will present you with your prize.

Yours faithfully,

J. Sexton

Mr Paul
10 Ma...
Saoc...

Paul jumped up. He danced round the kitchen and waved the letter from the newspaper.

'I've won!' he shouted. 'Mother, I've got the prize! I'll be a writer! We'll have some money at last! I'll buy you a new dress and some furniture for the house.' He stopped.

'Will Maria see my story in the paper?' he asked.

His mother looked at him. She was not smiling now.

'Do you still love that girl, Paul?' she asked.

'Yes, Mother,' said Paul 'I'll always love her.'

On Thursday, Paul went to the newspaper office. The manager was very friendly.

'Your story is good,' he said. 'Very good indeed. Here is the prize money.'

He gave Paul an envelope. £500! Paul did not believe it. He thanked the manager and started to go.

'Don't go,' said the manager. 'I want to talk to you. What's your job?'

'I haven't got a job, sir,' said Paul. 'I want to be a writer.'

'Good,' said the manager. 'We need young men like you. Come and work on our newspaper.'

Paul was very surprised.

'You want me? On your newspaper? Yes! Yes, of course I'll come,' he said.

Part 3

Paul loved his work on the newspaper. He worked hard, but he did not forget Maria.

One day, a reporter came into the office.

'Listen everybody,' he said. 'Here's a story for the paper. Do you remember that beautiful girl, Maria, and her rich husband? There was a photograph of the wedding in our paper. She ran away from her husband last week!'

Everybody in the office stopped talking. This was news! Paul sat still. He felt cold.

Maria left her husband! he thought. Why? They were married only a few months ago.

The reporter was still talking.

'The girl's mother died last week,' he said. 'She heard the news and the shock killed her.'

That ugly old woman, thought Paul.

'The mother was rich, wasn't she?' somebody asked.

'Oh yes, she was very rich,' said the reporter. 'Maria will have all her money, of course. And her husband gave her a lot of money, clothes, jewels, and a car. Maria is a very, very rich woman.'

'I don't like rich women,' said another reporter.

'Maria is rich,' said Paul. 'But she is also gentle and kind and . . .' he stopped.

'Do you know Maria?' the reporter asked.

'Yes,' said Paul quietly. 'I know Maria.'

'Well,' said the reporter, 'somebody must go to her mother's funeral. We need a report about it for the paper. Why don't you go, Paul?'

———

Paul went to the funeral the next day. It was a long way to the church, but he walked. He wanted to think.

Maria loved me, he thought. But she married another man. Why? Because she was afraid of her mother. But now, her mother is dead!

Paul was happy and he was sad. He was at the church now. Crowds of people were there. It was a big funeral.

There were many big, black cars outside the church. In the first one was the coffin. There were a lot of flowers on the coffin and on the roof of the car.

Paul stood at the back of the crowd. He took out his pencil and paper. He wrote about the cars and the people.

Then he saw Maria. She was wearing a black dress. She looked sad, but very beautiful. She was standing alone. Nobody spoke to her. Nobody went near her.

The man next to Paul spoke.

'That's the daughter,' he said. 'She's a bad woman. She left her husband and it killed her mother. Look at her! Nobody wants to speak to her.'

Paul said nothing.

Poor Maria, he thought.

Everybody went inside the church. The funeral began.

After the funeral, Paul went home. His mother was smiling.

'Good news, Paul,' she said. 'Do you remember your cousin, Elsa? She is coming to stay with us. She is seventeen now, and very pretty. You will like her.'

'Yes, I remember Elsa,' said Paul. He did not look pleased.

His mother was disappointed.

He is still thinking about Maria, she thought. Elsa will help him to forget.

But Paul did not want to see Elsa.

I must see Maria, he said to himself. I must talk to her.

Part 4

Paul wanted to see Maria. He wanted to talk to her.

I'll go to the house on the hill, he thought. Perhaps Maria will be there.

But the house on the hill looked empty. There were no curtains at the windows. There was a big notice on the gate. It said "For Sale".

Paul looked over the gate. There was nobody in the garden. Everything was quiet.

I'll get into the house and look round, he thought. Perhaps I'll find Maria's address. Then I can write to her.

Paul pushed open the gate, and went up the steps to the house. It was very quiet. He pushed at the front door. It was closed. He walked round the house. There was a window open.

Quickly, Paul climbed through the open window. He was excited and his heart was beating fast. He was in Maria's old home! He remembered her mother. He remembered that terrible evening. But the house was different now. There was no furniture in the room. There were no carpets and pictures. It was empty.

Paul felt a little afraid.

Is anybody in the house? he thought. No, he did not hear anything.

Quietly, Paul went to the door of the room and opened it. There was nobody there. He went from room to room. All the rooms were big, and they were all empty.

At last he came to a very big room. He stopped. He knew this room. He had met Maria's mother here! He remembered everything, the old woman, her hard face, the big rings on her hands . . . And now the old woman was dead.

Suddenly, Paul heard a noise. Somebody was inside the room! The door opened. Somebody was standing in the doorway. It was a woman.

'Maria!' said Paul.
'Paul!' Maria said. 'What are you doing here?'
'I was looking for you,' said Paul.
'You were looking for me?' asked Maria. She smiled.

'Maria,' said Paul. 'Why did you marry that man?'

'Mother was old,' said Maria. 'I was unhappy here. I never went to parties, never went out. I wanted money. I wanted a good time and friends.'

'I understand,' Paul said. 'You were not afraid of your mother. You were tired of her. She was old, and you wanted a new life. But why did you leave your husband?'

'My husband?' said Maria. 'That fat old man! He was stupid, Paul. He gave me money. He gave me jewels, a car . . . everything. But he didn't like my friends. He liked old people. I like clever, young people, Paul. I like you. You understand, don't you?'

'Yes,' said Paul slowly. 'I understand now.'

'I'm glad,' said Maria. 'I was unhappy about you, Paul. I liked you. I liked your funny poems . . .'

'My funny poems . . .' said Paul. He stopped.

'You loved me, didn't you, Paul?' said Maria. 'Do you still love me?'

'You are married,' said Paul. 'You have a husband.'

'But I don't love him,' said Maria quickly. 'I want to be free. I want to go to parties and enjoy myself. Come with me. I have money now. We'll be happy together.'

'No,' said Paul. 'No. Everything's over.'

Maria was angry. Her eyes were small and cold, and her mouth was thin and hard. Her hands were covered with big rings. Maria looked like her mother.

'I'm sorry Maria,' he said. 'I don't love you any more. I loved you very much, but now everything is different. Goodbye, Maria.'

'But you can't leave me,' said Maria. 'I *want* you.'

'Go back to your husband,' said Paul.

He looked at her for the last time. Then he turned, and walked out of the room. Paul left the house on the hill, and walked home. He was free.

I was a fool, he thought. Maria never loved me. How stupid I was! Maria is beautiful, but she is hard and cold. She is like her mother. I loved Maria's beauty. But I never loved Maria.

It was a lovely evening. Paul felt very happy. The door of the little brown house was open. His mother was at home. She was talking to a pretty girl.

'Paul,' she said, 'this is your cousin, Elsa.'

'Hello Elsa,' said Paul. He smiled.

Published by Macmillan Heinemann ELT
Between Towns Road, Oxford OX4 3PP
Macmillan Heinemann ELT is an imprint of
Macmillan Publishers Limited
Companies and representatives throughout the world
Heinemann is a registered trademark of Pearson Education, used under licence.

ISBN 978 0 2300 3504 1
ISBN 978 1 4050 7614 2 (with CD pack)

Text © Elizabeth Laird 1978, 1992, 2005
First published 1978

This edition first published 2005

Illustrated by Annie Farrall
Typography by Adrian Hodgkins
Original cover template design by Jackie Hill
Cover photography by Gabe Palmer/Corbis

Printed in Thailand

2010   2009   2008
5   4   3   2   1

with CD pack

2012   2011   2010
10   9   8   7